Peter Pan

J. M. Barrie was born in Scotland, the ninth child in his family. When he was older, and had moved to London, he went for a seaside holiday with some friends. While they were there, he organised a two-week-long game on the beach for the children – a game including shipwrecks, gangplanks, pirates and fairies. From this game the story of *Peter Pan* was born. And every time someone buys a book about Peter Pan, some money goes to the Great Ormond Street Hospital for Sick Children. This was J.M. Barrie's gift to all the lost boys that he would never know.

J.M. Barrie's

Peter Pan

Adapted by JOHN GOODWIN

Illustrated by Alan Marks

Contents

1

Peter Pan

Mr and Mrs Darling lived in a tall house in town with their three children, Wendy, John and Michael, and their big dog, Nana. Each night, Mrs Darling tucked them safely into bed in their nursery and wished them sweet dreams. And they seemed to have them.

But one night, as the Darling children were just about to go to sleep, Mrs Darling found some strange leaves on the nursery floor. The leaves had appeared from nowhere. They certainly hadn't been there when the children had climbed into their beds. Mrs Darling was puzzling over them when Wendy, the oldest of the children, said sleepily,

'That's Peter again.'

Mrs Darling looked hard at Wendy.

'Whatever do you mean?' she asked.

'It's Peter Pan,' said Wendy. 'He often comes to the nursery and talks to me.'

'Nonsense,' said Mrs Darling. 'No one can come into the house without knocking at the front door.'

'I think he comes in by the window,' said Wendy calmly.

'My love, the nursery is three floors up,' said Mrs Darling.

'But the leaves were by the window, weren't they?' said Wendy.

It was quite true; she had found the

leaves by the window. Mrs Darling looked at Wendy's freckled face again and into her clear blue eyes. Wendy was her only daughter and a sensible and thoughtful girl. She then looked towards her other children, John and Michael, who were sleeping soundly. Their heads of thick ginger hair lay still on their pillows. She knew the children made up stories. Sometimes they acted them out. To the children the land of make believe was real. They called it Neverland.

In Neverland brilliant adventures happen all day long. There are coral reefs and magical boats. Gnomes can be found, and princes, as well as an old lady with a hooked nose. On the magic shores of Neverland children can play all day long. Mrs Darling had been to Neverland when she was a child. Sometimes she still heard the sound of its surf breaking on the shore – though it was very faint and far in the distance.

Mrs Darling picked up one of the leaves and looked at it carefully. It was a brown autumn leaf. She was sure it did not come from any tree that grew in Britain. Mrs Darling crawled about the floor, peering with a candle for any marks of strange feet. She rattled the poker up the chimney and tapped the walls. Surely Wendy had been dreaming. Of course Wendy

had been dreaming. There was no sign of any stranger in the nursery.

All the children were fast asleep as she sat down to do her sewing. Mr Darling was working late in the city and she was tired. Nana, the Newfoundland dog who was trained to look after the children, was sleeping in the room below. The nursery was warm and cosy, and Mrs Darling soon nodded off to sleep.

While she slept she had a dream. She dreamt that Neverland had come to life and that a strange boy had come to visit. While she dreamt, the window of the nursery blew open, and a small boy appeared. With him came a strange light which was no bigger than your fist. The light darted about the room like a living thing and woke up Mrs Darling.

She started with a cry and saw the boy. He was dressed in autumn leaves, and his

white teeth shone like pearls. She knew at
once that it was Peter Pan.

2

The shadow

Mrs Darling screamed and screamed though all the children slept on soundly. Nana woke up from the room below and bounded into the nursery. She growled and sprang at the boy, who leapt lightly out through the window. Again Mrs Darling screamed, thinking that Nana had hurt Peter Pan. She ran down into the street below to look for the little boy, but she couldn't find him anywhere.

She returned to the nursery and found Nana with something in her mouth. It was Peter Pan's shadow! Mrs Darling examined it closely. She didn't know what to do with it, and finally she carefully put it away in a drawer. She wanted to tell Mr Darling about everything that had happened, but he worked late every night at his job in the city. He always seemed far too busy to talk to her.

It was a whole week before Mrs Darling could speak to her husband. On Friday night he came home early. It was a never-to-be forgotten Friday night.

'Come on, we're going out,' he said. 'Get ready at once.'

Mrs Darling rushed off to change. All thoughts of speaking about the shadow in the drawer vanished from her mind – when Mr Darling decided to go out everything else had to wait.

Before Mr and Mrs Darling left the house it was an ordinary Friday, just like any other. Nana looked after the children just like she always did. She ran the water for Michael's bath and carried him to it on her back.

'I won't go to bed,' shouted Michael. 'I don't want a bath. I won't. I won't.'

Meanwhile, Mr and Mrs Darling were getting ready to go out. Mrs Darling looked beautiful in her fine dress. Mr Darling was grumpy as usual. He could not tie up his tie.

'How can I go out looking like this?' he complained.

With calm hands, Mrs Darling knotted his tie perfectly in a few seconds. Then Mr Darling tried to give Michael the night-time medicine for his cough. But Michael pulled his mouth away at the last moment.

'Won't. Won't,' he cried.

'Come on, Michael. Take it like a man,' said Mr Darling.

But Michael cried even louder. Mrs Darling rushed off to find him a chocolate to make the medicine taste sweeter.

'Don't pamper him! When I was his age I took medicine without any fuss,' shouted Mr Darling.

When she returned, Michael said he would only take the medicine if Nana gave it to him. Then Mr Darling lost his temper. Trying to show he was the master of the house, he dragged Nana out of the nursery and chained her up in her kennel outside.

Mrs Darling put the children to bed in silence. They could hear Nana barking and whimpering out in the yard.

'That's not Nana's unhappy bark,' said Wendy. 'That's her bark when she smells danger.'

The word 'danger' ran straight to Mrs Darling's heart.

'Are you sure, Wendy?' she said.

'Oh, yes,' answered Wendy.

Mrs Darling went to the window and looked out. The sky was full of stars.

'Oh, how I wish that we weren't going out tonight,' she said.

'Can anything harm us?' asked Michael, half asleep.

'Of course not,' said Mrs Darling. 'You have Nana to guard you.'

'Stop fussing. Hurry up or we'll be late,' said Mr Darling.

Then the parents were gone. They stepped out of the silent house and into the night air. There had been a slight fall of snow and they picked their way through it carefully, trying not to spoil their shoes. All the stars in the night sky were watching them.

The stars were beautiful, but all they could do was watch and twinkle. This is the punishment that all stars suffer for something they did so long ago that no star remembers what it was. So the older ones have become glassy-eyed and rarely speak. Winking is the star language. But the little stars are still bright and alert. Peter Pan often flies among them. They are not always friendly to him, because he has a mischievous way of stealing up behind them and trying to blow them out. Tonight, though, they are on his side, and looking forward to the fun, just waiting for the grown-ups to get out of the way.

So, as soon as Mr and Mrs Darling left the house, the smallest of the stars in the Milky Way screamed out:

'Now, Peter!'

3

Come away, come away

For a minute after Mr and Mrs Darling walked out of their house, everything was just as they had left it. Up in the nursery it was quiet. All the children were asleep. Then the flames of the three candles next to each of their beds began to flicker. First one candle went out and then a second. When the third candle flame flickered out, the room became dark.

But it was only for a second. Another light, a thousand times brighter than any candle flame, was shining in the nursery. The light darted around the room. It went into the wardrobe and in every drawer of the chest of drawers. It was looking for Peter's shadow. As it searched, it threw things in all directions. Soon clothes of every kind were scattered all over the floor.

If you looked very closely at the light you could see it was not a light at all, but a fairy no bigger than your hand. The fairy's name was Tinker Bell. A few seconds after the fairy's entrance, the window of the nursery was blown wide open and in flew Peter Pan.

'Tinker Bell?' whispered Peter, making sure he did not wake the sleeping children.

'Tinker Bell, where are you?' he whispered again.

Then Peter saw Tinker Bell hiding inside

a jug. He could see the tips of her tiny feathery wings sticking out just above the rim.

'Come out of that jug,' he said. 'Do you know where they put my shadow?'

A sound like a tiny tinkle of a golden bell answered him. It was Tinker Bell talking in fairy language. It is such a strange sound that no human child can understand it.

Tinker Bell told Peter that his shadow was in the chest of drawers. Peter immediately jumped into the drawers, scattering more clothes on the floor. He soon found his shadow and was so pleased that he closed the drawer without thinking, and trapped Tinker Bell inside it.

With a few neat strides he was in the bathroom, trying to stick his shadow back on with soap. He rubbed and rubbed at the soap. But it was hopeless. He couldn't stick his shadow back on and was so upset that he sat on the floor and cried.

His crying woke Wendy, who sat up in bed looking at him. She didn't feel scared that this odd little boy was in the nursery.

'Why are you crying?' she asked.

Peter looked at her. Then he stopped crying, stood up and gave a polite bow.

'What's your name?' he said, looking at her slender face.

'Wendy Moira Angela Darling,' she

replied. 'I know yours. It's Peter Pan. Where do you live?'

'Second to the right and then straight on till morning,' said Peter.

Wendy had never heard of an address like that before. 'What a funny address,' she said. 'Is that where they take the letters you get in the post?'

'I don't get any letters,' said Peter.

'What about your mother's letters?' asked Wendy.

'I don't have a mother,' he said.

Wendy looked at his unhappy face. 'No wonder you are sad,' she said.

'I wasn't crying about mothers,' he said. 'I was crying about this.'

He held up his crumpled shadow. When Wendy saw it she knew what to do straight away.

'I'll sew it back on,' she said.

Peter looked puzzled.

'What's *sew*?' he asked.

'Watch,' said Wendy, as she quickly stitched it back on with a needle and cotton. Peter danced round the room happily.

'Wendy, you are such a clever girl,' he said. 'One girl is more use than twenty boys!'

'That's very kind of you,' said Wendy. 'I'll give you a kiss if you like.'

Peter looked more puzzled than ever. 'What's a kiss?' he asked.

'I'll show you,' said Wendy.

She closed her eyes and moved closer to Peter. Peter backed away. Instead of finding him she felt something pushed into her hand. She opened her eyes to see it was a button made out of an acorn.

'It's a present,' he said. 'For sewing back my shadow.'

'It's beautiful,' she said. 'I'll put it on a chain and wear it round my neck. Thank you, Peter.'

Then she held out her hand. 'I'll shake

your hand just like grown-ups do.'

Peter backed away again.

'No,' he said. 'I don't ever want to be grown up. I want to be a little boy for ever and have fun. That's what I've always wanted. It's why I live among fairies.'

Wendy sat quite still while Peter told her more about fairies.

'When the first baby laughed for the first time, its laugh broke into a thousand pieces. All those thousand pieces skipped about and turned into fairies,' he said.

Then he looked sad again.

'But many children today don't believe in fairies. Every time one of them says "I don't believe in fairies", then somewhere a fairy dies.'

At that moment Peter remembered Tinker Bell. He must have shut her away in the drawer. He let poor Tinker Bell out and said to her, 'This is Wendy. I'm telling her all about fairies.'

But Tinker Bell was in a bad temper by now and said in fairy language that Wendy was a big, ugly girl. So Peter and Wendy ignored her and carried on talking.

'Where do you live now?' said Wendy.

'With the lost boys,' said Peter.

'Who are they?' asked Wendy.

'They are babies who fall out of their prams when their parents are looking the other way. If their parents don't find them within seven days they are sent far off to Neverland. I'm the captain of Neverland,' said Peter.

'It must be fun,' said Wendy.

'It is,' said Peter. 'But we are rather lonely. There are no girls in Neverland. Will you come to Neverland, Wendy, and look after us all?'

'Oh, I can't,' said Wendy. 'How would I get there?'

'You'd fly there,' said Peter. 'It's easy to fly. I'll teach you. You just jump on the wind's back and away you go.'

Wendy looked over to John and Michael's beds.

'Will you teach John and Michael to fly too?' she asked.

'If you like,' said Peter.

Wendy ran over to their beds and shook them awake.

'Wake up,' she cried. 'Peter Pan has come. He's going to teach us how to fly.'

At first the boys grumbled at being woken up but they soon became very excited by the idea of flying. Just as Peter started to teach them, Wendy felt something pulling her hair. It was Tinker Bell, showing her bad temper. She was jealous of all the attention Wendy was getting from Peter. Wendy cried out in pain.

Out in the yard, Nana heard Wendy's cry of pain. Nana pulled and pulled at her chain until at last she broke it. She ran down the street at once to the house where Mr and Mrs Darling were guests at a party. She howled and barked outside the front door and Mr and Mrs Darling came running outside at once. They knew something must be very wrong in the nursery.

But Peter Pan was working quickly. He blew a handful of fairy dust on to the three children. Immediately their bodies began to rise up into the air.

'Look at me!'

'Look at *me*!'

'I can fly!' they cried.

By now their heads were right up to the ceiling.

'Ready for our journey to Neverland?' said Peter.

'Ready!' said the three airborne children.

The nursery window was open, so away they flew into the night sky. At that moment Mr and Mrs Darling rushed into the nursery with Nana barking furiously by their side. But it was too late. The children had flown away.

4

The flight

'Second to the right and then straight on till morning.'

That was the way to Neverland. The three children found flying brilliant fun. They swooped about tall buildings to show off their skill, and circled round church spires, office blocks and very tall trees on their way to Neverland.

John and Michael flew off like rockets.

They raced each other with Michael in front. But the way to Neverland was no quick sprint. It was a long long journey. Soon they were flying over the sea. Time and distance were unclear. Sometimes it was dark and sometimes light. Sometimes they were very cold. Then they were very hot. They tried not to be sleepy but the longer they flew the more tired they became.

Peter had a game for feeding them. He would fly after birds with food in their beaks. He would then swoop and snatch the food from them. Then the birds would snatch it back. In this crazy chase the miles passed and Neverland grew a little closer – though no one got much to eat!

Suddenly Michael fell asleep. It was bound to happen. Straight away he fell down towards the sea far below.

Wendy shrieked out, 'Save him, Peter! Save him!'

Peter just chuckled with laughter – this was another game to him. Wendy cried out even louder.

'Please save him!'

After a few more agonising seconds Peter dived through the air and caught Michael, just before he hit the choppy waters of the deep blue sea. Both Michael and John fell again because they were so tired. Each time, Peter would leave it till the last minute to rescue them. The other game Peter played was to fly very close to the waves of the sea, running his finger along each passing shark's tail. When he did this the three children lost sight of him for a long time.

Wendy was really worried. 'What would we do if Peter didn't come back?' she asked.

'We'd go home,' said Michael.

'How would we find our way?' asked Wendy.

'And how would we land?' said John. 'Peter has forgotten to show us how.'

But they didn't have to worry, for just then Peter zoomed back towards them. He taught them how to stretch out flat on their backs on a strong wind and let it carry them along. Once they were used to this it became easy. They could even sleep like this without falling. Each of the three children had just fallen into a safe deep sleep on the back of the wind when Peter shouted, 'We get off here.'

They all woke with a start.

'There it is,' said Peter.

'Where? Where?' they cried.

'Where all the golden arrows are pointing,' said Peter.

Golden beams of sun filled the sky and each beam pointed like an arrow in the same direction. Wendy, John and Michael balanced on tiptoe, peering into the distance. Then they all saw the island at

the same moment. The clouds parted and, below them, they recognised the place of their dreams – Neverland.

It was a sight so amazing that the three children knew they would never forget it. They could just make out a huge forest, and a sparkling river winding through it. They thought they saw wild animals picking their way through the trees, and mermaids basking in a lagoon, combing their hair. Because it was a magical island, it looked like it was wintertime on the river and summertime on the lagoon.

'Look at the turtles burying their eggs in the sand!' cried John.

'There's the boat that I sail in my dreams,' shouted Michael.

'I can see smoke!' cried Wendy.

'Where?' shouted John and Michael.

'There, by the hunters' camp,' said Wendy.

When they were right over Neverland they could see everything much more clearly. There were animals and people moving everywhere. All the animals seemed to be trying to keep out of the way of a party of hunters. The hunters were looking out for pirates. The pirates were looking out for the lost boys. All these different groups were chasing each other all over the island.

Up in the sky it was growing darker quickly. The three children huddled close to Peter.

'They don't want us to land,' said Peter.

'Who are *they*?' asked Wendy.

Instead of answering, Peter asked another question.

'There's a pirate just below us, hiding in the tall grass. Shall we go down and scare him?'

'What are pirates?' asked Michael.

'Pirates are evil,' said Peter. 'They steal ships and kidnap people. Their captain is James Hook.'

The boys could tell Peter hated saying the word 'Hook' and they moved closer to Wendy.

'He is the nastiest pirate that ever lived,' said Peter.

'What's he like?' asked John. 'Is he big?'

'Not as big as he was,' said Peter.

'How do you mean?' asked Wendy.

'I cut a bit off him,' said Peter.

'How?' asked John.

'Which bit?' asked Michael.

'His right hand,' said Peter.

'So he can't fight now?' said Wendy.

'Oh, he can still fight,' said Peter.

'How?' asked John again.

'He has an iron hook instead of a right hand. He claws with it,' said Peter.

'Claws?' said Michael, in a trembly voice.

'Yes. His iron claw is terrible,' said Peter. 'But I am not afraid of Hook. I will fight him any day.'

All the children looked at Peter in admiration.

'Every person that serves under me,' Peter continued, 'has to promise . . .'

'What?' asked Michael. 'What do we promise?'

'If you meet Captain Hook in open fight, you must leave him to me.'

'I promise,' said John and Michael both together.

By this time it had grown even darker. Wendy heard a sound like the tiny tinkling of a little bell. She knew that Tinker Bell was talking to Peter in fairy language. She'd flown with them all the way and had been grumpy the whole journey.

'What's she saying?' asked Wendy.

'She says that the pirates saw us before it went dark. They've got Long Tom out.'

'What's Long Tom?' asked Michael.

'It's a big cannon,' said Peter.

'Can't you tell Tinker Bell to go away?'

said Wendy. 'If the pirates see her bright light surely they will fire at us.'

'I can't do that,' said Peter. 'Tinker Bell is very frightened.'

'Then maybe she could put out her light?' asked Wendy.

'She can't do that. Fairies can never put out their lights,' said Peter.

'Then what shall we do?' said Wendy, in panic.

'If only we had a pocket we could hide her in,' said Peter.

It was at that moment that John had a good idea. 'My hat! Hide her in there,' he shouted.

Wendy grabbed John's hat and thrust an angry Tinker Bell into it. Then the four travellers hovered in the darkness, wondering what their next move would be. Suddenly the air was ripped apart by a tremendous crash. The pirates had fired Long Tom. The blast of the cannon sent

Peter far out to sea. John and Michael found themselves alone in the dark, while Wendy was blown upwards. The hat – and Tinker bell – were torn clean out of Wendy's hand.

Now, Tinker Bell was so full of jealousy for Wendy that evil filled her heart to the brim. Fairies are either very good or very bad. They can't be half and half. Their tiny bodies haven't room for both. So, free from the hat, Tinker Bell flew alongside Wendy and whispered some magic words in fairy language into her ear. Though Wendy could not understand them, she found herself following Tinker Bell, not knowing that the fairy meant to harm her. They both plunged downwards. Lower and lower they fell, ever closer to the island. And still Wendy didn't suspect a thing.

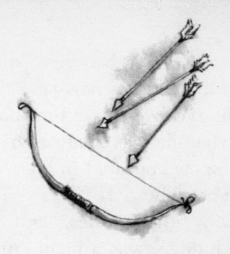

5

The island come true

Down below them, on the island of Neverland, Captain Hook sat on his pirate throne. The throne was hoisted into the air by members of his pirate gang – Juke, Starkey and his right-hand man, Smee. Only, of course, Hook didn't have a right hand at all, but an iron claw instead. They were the most terrible pirate gang you could ever imagine. Hook's hair was so long that it reached right down to his shoulders and was flowing with black curls. His eyes were forget-me-not blue, except when he was really angry. Then two red spots appeared in them and lit them up horribly.

Following the pirates, and trying to keep hidden, was a giant crocodile. Wherever Hook went, on land or sea, the

crocodile followed. When Peter Pan had cut off Hook's hand he'd thrown it to the crocodile. The creature had licked its lips and from then on had wanted to taste the rest of Hook. But luckily for Hook, the crocodile had swallowed a clock which went *tick tock, tick tock* inside him. So, whenever Hook heard the sound of the clock, he knew he'd better beware.

'Some day,' said Smee, 'that clock will run down and stop ticking, and then he'll get you.'

'Yes,' said Hook. 'That's the fear that haunts me.'

Also tracking the pirates were a gang of hunters. They carried tomahawks and knives and their bodies gleamed with paint and oil. Their leader was Great Big Little Panther. He was always at the front of the gang. At the rear, the most dangerous place, was their strange princess, Tiger Lily. The hunters stalked over fallen twigs without making the slightest noise. The only sound you could hear was their own breathing. Lions, tigers, bears and many other smaller animals roamed freely in Neverland, and the hunters tracked them all. But today they were tracking pirates.

The lost boys also roamed the island. They were Tootles, Nibs, Slightly, Curly and the twins. All the boys had sad eyes, uncombed hair, and dirty faces. They were dressed in ragged and tattered clothes.

'I do wish Peter would come back,' said every one of them nervously. They looked up to the sky for any sign of him. Tootles suddenly spotted something.

'Look there,' he cried.

All the boys peered upwards.

'It's a great white bird!' shouted Curly.

Then they saw it falling closer and closer to the ground. Next they heard a sad cry coming from the bird. But more clearly came the shrill voice of Tinker Bell.

'Hello, Tinker Bell,' shouted the lost boys. Unlike Wendy and her brothers, they could understand fairy language.

'Peter wants you to shoot this white Wendy bird,' replied Tinker Bell.

The lost boys never questioned Peter's orders.

'Let's do what Peter wants,' they said.

Before any of the others could move, Tootles had his bow and arrow ready.

'Quick, Tootles,' they cried. 'Peter will be so pleased.'

Tootles excitedly fitted the arrow to his bow.

'Out of the way, Tinker Bell,' he shouted.

Then he fired. Wendy fluttered to the ground and lay still.

Tootles was standing over Wendy's body. The rest of the boys darted out from the trees.

'I shot the Wendy bird,' he crowed.

Overhead, Tinker Bell saw what had happened and went into hiding. There was silence round the body on the ground. It was a terrible silence. All of them were too scared to speak. At last Slightly said, 'This isn't a bird. I think it's a girl.'

'A girl?' said Tootles, and he began to tremble.

'She's not moving,' said Nibs sadly.

They all took off their hats and bowed their heads.

'Peter was bringing this girl to us,' said Curly, as big tears rolled down his cheeks.

At that moment they heard a sound that made each of them tremble. Peter had arrived. He flew in and landed close to them saying, 'I'm back, boys. Why didn't you cheer when you saw me arrive?'

Not one of them spoke.

'Great news, boys!' said Peter. 'I've

brought you a mother to look after us all. Have you seen her? She was heading this way.'

Tootles stepped forward.

'She's here,' he said.

At last Peter saw Wendy's body on the ground. He knelt down at once and pulled the arrow from her breast.

'Who fired the arrow?' he asked, with tears in his eyes.

Tootles bowed his head again. 'I did,' he said.

At that moment, Wendy began to lift her arm very slowly. Nibs was the first to see it.

'Look!' he shouted.

'She's alive,' cried Peter.

He bent his head closer to her and saw that Wendy was wearing the acorn button he had given her on a chain round her neck. The arrow had hit the button and saved her life.

'Carry her into the house,' cried the twins together.

'No. No,' shouted Peter. 'We mustn't touch her – she's injured. We'll build a little house round her.'

Without further ado they set to and began building the house. They ran into their own underground house and dragged out bedding and firewood so that she would be as comfortable as possible. They were so busy that they hardly noticed John and Michael drifting to earth, still rather sleepy from their journey.

'John? Where's Mother and Nana?' mumbled Michael, whilst John asked 'Did we *really* fly?'

Then the two boys found Peter, who was standing close to Wendy.

'Is Wendy asleep?' they asked.

Peter didn't answer and told them to help with the house-building.

When at last the house was built around

her, Wendy opened her eyes.

'Where am I?' she asked.

Nibs was the first to speak to her.

'We built this house for you,' he said shyly.

'For shelter,' added Curly.

'And we're your little children,' said the twins, both together. That night Wendy slept safely in the little house. Peter kept guard outside with his sword drawn, for the noise of pirates could be heard far away and wolves were on the prowl. But inside the little house Wendy was warm and cosy and slowly getting better. And, in the morning, when she was well enough to move, she went down to join the rest of the children in their underground house.

6

A home under the ground

'The glass slipper just wouldn't fit the feet of the ugly sisters no matter how hard they pushed and pulled and struggled. That's when Cinderella came into the room.'

Wendy was telling a story. The lost boys were listening to her every word. You could have heard a pin drop in the cosy underground house. Tootles looked at Wendy with his big sad eyes whilst Curly kept very still. Slightly had even forgotten about playing the whistle he'd made from a hollow cane, and Nibs and Peter were unusually quiet. Both twins were almost asleep but wouldn't nod off until the story was finished. It was only Tinker Bell who didn't want to listen to Wendy but sat by herself in her own tiny bedroom. Peter was still refusing to speak to her after putting Wendy's life in danger.

Everyone was safe in the snug simple underground house. Peter had shown the three children how to enter the house down a hollow tree. Everybody had their own special tree entrance, which they fitted through exactly. Once inside their tree, they zoomed down the hollow trunk, to land with a bump on the floor of the underground house. John and Michael liked zooming up and down so much they flew in and out of their trees all day long. But Peter made it clear to them that the hollow trees were for getting home safely – not for playing in. When danger was nearby, they had to escape down them and into the house as fast as they could.

Wendy stayed in the underground house for days and rarely went out at all. She cooked the meals. They ate roasted bread fruit, yams, baked pig, mammee-apples, tappa rolls and bananas washed down with calabashes of coconut milk. Every day ended with a special bed-time story from Wendy. The lost boys never tired of listening to them.

As time wore on she missed her own parents, Nana and the nursery, and she often thought of them. It's difficult to say how long the children stayed in the underground house. Time in Neverland is a strange thing. It may be measured by moons and suns like we measure days. But in Neverland there are many more suns and moons so it's hard to know exactly how fast the days are passing. John and Michael became confused too and Michael began to think that Wendy was his mother, not his sister at all.

When Wendy did leave the underground house, she would often go to sit by the lagoon and watch the sun set. The vivid blue water turned a fiery-red as the sun lowered in the sky, and mermaids

came and sang at the water's edge.

Wendy would sneak quietly to the edge of the water, hoping to see them. Their favourite place was Marooners' Rock, where they loved to bask in the sunshine. They would comb their hair and laze around all day long. Sometimes Wendy would swim silently out to them as close as she could. But the mermaids were not always friendly. When they saw her they all dived off the rock, splashing her with as much water as they could.

They treated all the boys just the same, except Peter, who chattered to them on the rock. He used to sit on their tails in a cheeky game and they never seemed to mind. Peter gave Wendy a wonderful present – a mermaid's comb for her own hair. They would never have given her one themselves, but somehow Peter always won them round.

7

The mermaid's lagoon

The most magical time to see the lagoon was by moonlight. Then the mermaids made strange wailing cries. It was also a dangerous time for children to be there.

All the children went to the lagoon one day when it was very hot and sunny. They sat together on Marooners' Rock in the warm sunshine, and one by one they fell asleep. That is, all except Wendy. She was enjoying gazing into the deep blue water while the others slept around her. Suddenly the sun went in, and shadows stole across the water. Wendy started to shiver, for the lagoon no longer seemed so friendly.

She knew it was not night-time that had arrived, but something as dark and more strange. What was happening? Her mind was full of the stories Peter had told her about Marooners' Rock. In the stories, evil captains chained sailors on the rock and left them there for ever. When the tide rose there was no escape from the rising water, as the whole rock sank below it.

Wendy knew she should wake the sleeping children at once. Then she heard the sound of muffled oars. A boat was drawing near. Where had the boat come from? Who was rowing it across the water? She wanted to cry out but when she opened her mouth she found she couldn't speak.

Peter suddenly woke from his sleep and sprang to his feet. With one warning cry he woke the others. He sensed that danger was near. He stood very still with one hand to his ear.

'Pirates!' he shouted.

All the children huddled close to him. A strange smile was playing on his face, which meant a fight might be just about to begin. Wendy saw the smile and shuddered. Peter then barked out an order like a captain in a battle.

'Dive!'

In an instant all the children dived into the water. Marooners' Rock and the water around it appeared deserted.

The boat with the muffled oars drew nearer. It was a pirate dinghy with three figures in it. Two were the pirates, Smee and Starkey, and the third was a prisoner – Tiger Lily, princess of the hunters. She

stared out across the water, knowing that her fate was to be left on Marooners' Rock.

'Easy there,' said Smee, as the pirates' dinghy bumped into the rock. The two men climbed out and on to the rock.

'Haul her out,' shouted Starkey.

Tiger Lily did not try to struggle or fight as the two pirates pulled her on to the rock. She was the proud daughter of a chief and would not show any fear. Once Tiger Lily was on the rock, Starkey shouted at her, 'This will teach you to prowl round our ship!'

'It's the Captain's orders,' said Smee, feeling a little sorry for her.

A short distance away from the rock, the heads of Wendy and Peter bobbed out of the water.

'What was that?' cried Smee.

'What was what?' said Starkey.

It was time for another of Peter's games. He shouted out in a voice which sounded very much like Hook's, 'Ahoy there, lubbers!'

Both Smee and Starkey were taken in by Peter's clever imitation.

'It's the Captain,' said Starkey. 'He must be swimming out to us from the ship.'

'We've got the princess on the rock,' shouted Smee.

'Set her free,' shouted back Peter, sounding more like Hook than ever.

'Free?' shouted the pirates, confused.

'Yes, let her go.'

'But Captain . . .'

'Do it now, or you'll feel my hook,' shouted Peter.

'Better do what he says,' said Starkey.

'Aye, aye,' said Smee, as he set Tiger Lily free. At once she slid into the water like an eel, a free princess again. Then the two pirates climbed back into their dinghy. Still bobbing about in the water, Wendy couldn't help crying out at the triumph of Peter's trick. But the joy of success was short-lived as another voice rang out across the lagoon, 'Ahoy there!'

It was the real Captain Hook. Peter gave a whistle of surprise.

'Ahoy there,' cried Hook again.

Now Wendy understood. Hook was also swimming in the water and was close to the pirate boat. In the light of the dinghy's lantern Wendy saw his hook grip the boat's side. Then she saw his swarthy face as he rose dripping out of the water and into the dinghy to join the other two pirates.

'Those boys have found a mother,' said Hook. 'I've heard her name is Wendy.'

Wendy started to shake with fear in the water. Peter gently pulled her down below the surface, worried that she would cry out and give the game away.

'Can't we kidnap this Wendy and make her our own mother?' said Smee.

'That's a princely plan,' said Hook. 'We'll capture *all* the children. We'll make the boys walk the plank and Wendy shall be our mother.'

By this time Wendy had bobbed up in the water again.

'Never!' she cried.

In the dinghy the pirates were startled.

'What was that?' said Hook.

Smee held up the lantern and they all looked about the dark water, but they couldn't see anyone.

'We heard a noise like that when we let the princess go,' said Starkey, puzzled.

'You let her go?' screamed Hook.

'You called us over the water to let her go,' said Starkey.

'I gave no such order!,' screamed Hook.

'Then who did?' said Smee.

Hook sat very still. 'There is a spirit that haunts this dark lagoon at night,' he muttered.

It was a moment which Peter couldn't resist. Imitating Hook again he cried, 'I am James Hook. Captain of the *Jolly Roger*.'

'You are not. *I* am Hook,' yelled Hook.

Smee and Starkey were really scared.

'I am Hook but I have another voice,' said Peter.

'What other voice?' said Hook.

'Guess,' said Peter.

'I can't guess,' said Hook. 'I can't.'

'You can,' said Peter. 'I am the voice of a boy.'

'Boy?'

'Yes.'

'An ordinary boy?' asked Hook.

'No.'

'What sort of a boy?'

'A wonderful boy!' said Wendy.

'A wonderful boy?' repeated Hook, still bewildered.

'Can't guess, can't guess,' chanted Peter. 'Do you give up?'

'Yes.'

'I am Peter Pan,' said Peter.

'Pan!' roared Hook.

In a second all three pirates had recovered themselves and spotted him in the water.

'Now we have him,' shouted Hook. 'Into the water, Smee. Starkey, mind the boat. Take him men – dead or alive!'

Smee and Hook dived into the water, heading for Peter Pan.

'Are you ready, boys?' shouted Peter.

'Yes. Yes,' shouted the excited voices of the boys from all over the lagoon.

Then the fight began. John gallantly climbed into the boat and held Starkey. The two struggled and then both fell into the water, leaving the dinghy to drift away. All this time Peter was swimming closer to Marooners' Rock. Hook rose by the rock to breathe and at the same moment Peter began to scale it from the opposite side.

Neither knew the other was coming. They came face to face with each other and froze in surprise.

Peter was the first to move. He snatched the knife out of Hook's belt and jumped up on top of the rock. Wanting a fair fight, he held out his hand to help Hook to bring him up on to the same level.

It was then that Hook bit his hand and threw him off guard. Then Hook hit him twice with his iron claw. Before Peter had a chance come back at him, Hook had disappeared. A few minutes later the boys saw him in the water. He'd seen the giant crocodile and was now swimming wildly towards the *Jolly Roger*, which was anchored nearby. He was white with fear because the crocodile was catching up with him fast. When all three pirates had fled the scene, the boys called out, 'Wendy! Peter! Wendy! Peter!'

But no answer came. At last they found

the empty pirate dinghy, and still calling out to Peter and Wendy, they rowed home.

'Wendy and Peter must be swimming back, or flying,' said Tootles.

A feeble cry for help came from the rock.

But it was too quiet for anyone to hear. Wendy was exhausted from being in the water for such a long time and Peter had been wounded by Hook's claw. And the rock they sat on was getting smaller and smaller.

'The water's rising, Wendy,' said Peter. 'It will soon be right over us. We must leave.'

'I'm exhausted,' said Wendy.

'We must fly or swim,' said Peter, trying to gather up all the energy he had left.

'I don't think I can,' said Wendy, weakly.

At that moment something brushed lightly past Peter. It was the tail of a kite Michael had made some days earlier and lost that afternoon.

'Michael's kite,' said Peter. 'It lifted him off the ground. Why shouldn't it carry both of us off this rock?'

'It might carry one of us, but not both,' said Wendy quietly. 'The twins tried it and failed.'

Peter lifted Wendy to her feet. 'You go,' he said.

'No,' cried Wendy, holding on to him and the tail of the kite.

But Peter was the stronger of the two.

'Goodbye, Wendy,' he said, as he pushed her off the rock and into the path of the wind. In a few minutes she was carried away and out of sight.

Peter was left alone on the rock, which was by now very small indeed. Soon it would be entirely below the water. Pale rays of light tiptoed across the lagoon as the most musical and strange sounds in the world rose into the air. The mermaids were calling to the moon.

8

The Never Bird

By now the water was nibbling at Peter's feet. He was watching the only moving thing on the lagoon, which he thought was a floating piece of paper.

'Perhaps it's part of the kite,' he said to himself.

As he watched it, he thought it seemed to be fighting a battle with the oncoming tide. But it was not a piece of paper at all –

it was the Never Bird, floating on her nest, making a desperate effort to reach him across the water. Her nest was like a tiny boat which was thrown this way and that by the tide.

'I – want – to save – you,' she cried.

But she was speaking in a strange language and Peter couldn't understand it. With one last huge effort the bird propelled her nest against the rock. Then up she flew, deserting her eggs which lay snugly in the nest. At last Peter understood – the Never Bird was trying to rescue him, and had even deserted her eggs to save his life. She hovered overhead as Peter looked at the two white eggs in the nest.

Peter saw that one of the pirates had left his hat on the rock. So he gently placed the eggs in the hat and put the hat on the water. It floated beautifully. Then Peter climbed carefully into the nest and, waving his thanks to the Never Bird, was carried away to safety by the wind. The Never Bird sat happily on her eggs in the hat and drifted off home.

When Peter at last reached the underground house everyone was so relieved to see him. What an adventure they'd all had!

After Peter's bravery in saving Tiger Lily, the hunters were ready to show their loyalty in return. They gave Peter the special name of the Great White Father and danced in his honour. Then they all took up posts to guard the children's house.

Down below them, in the underground house, Wendy told the children another of her favourite bed-time stories. It was the story that the boys loved best, and Peter hated most. Usually when she began to tell this story he either went outside or put his hands over his ears. But on this evening he sat still and listened.

Wendy began, 'There was once a man whose name was Mr Darling . . .'

'I know this story,' said John.

Wendy continued, 'and his wife was called Mrs Darling.'

'I think I know her,' said Michael, trying hard to remember his mother and father.

Wendy carried on. 'They had three children,' she said. Then she sighed rather sadly.

'These children,' she continued, 'had a faithful dog called Nana, who looked after them – how they loved that dog. One day, when Mr Darling was very angry, he chained Nana up in the yard: and so all the children left home. They flew to Neverland where the lost boys are. When Mr and Mrs Darling came home, all they found were three empty beds. But

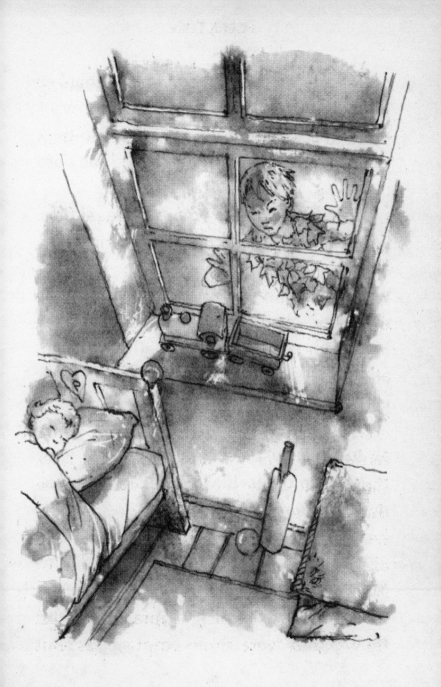

one of the children, Wendy, knows that her mother will always keep the window of the nursery open for the children, so they can fly back into the house when they are ready.'

Peter stood up from where he was sitting.

'Wendy, you are wrong about mothers,' he said. 'Long ago, I thought the window of *my* bedroom would always be open for me. Then when I flew back, it was locked. My mother had forgotten all about me, and another little boy was sleeping in my bed.'

There was silence in the little house and all the lost boys looked very sad.

'Are all mothers like that?' asked Tootles, in a miserable voice.

'Yes,' replied Peter firmly.

'Wendy, let's go home,' said John and Michael together.

'Not tonight,' said Curly. 'Please don't go tonight.'

The lost boys were so shocked at the thought of losing Wendy that they all crowded around her.

'It will be awful without you,' they said. 'Don't go.'

'We shan't let her go,' said Curly angrily. 'We'll keep her prisoner.'

Wendy turned to Tootles in desperation.

'Tootles, you are the kindest boy here. Please let me go,' she said.

Tootles spoke straight away.

'We must let her go,' he said firmly.

Peter had been quiet whilst all this was happening. He now said sadly, 'The hunters will guide you through the woods. Then Tinker Bell will fly with you across the sea.'

Wendy looked at all the lost boys in turn.

'Why don't you all come back with us?' she said. 'I am sure my father and mother would look after you.'

The boys turned to Peter. 'Can we go?' they pleaded.

'If you want to,' said Peter, without smiling.

Immediately they all rushed off to pack their things.

'Will you get your things too, Peter?' asked Wendy, gently.

'No,' said Peter. 'I'm not coming with you.'

'Please come, Peter,' cried Wendy. 'You can find your mother.'

Peter got up slowly.

'I'm tired,' he said. 'I'm going to bed.'

9

Do you believe?

In the darkness of the night, everything was silent. Everything was still. But someone was moving very slowly and quietly along the path. Footsteps could be heard faintly. Then more – and more. The pirates were on the move. Carefully and cautiously they crept up on the hunters' camp.

When the pirates were within a short

distance of the hunters, Hook held up his hand. It was the signal for silence. The pirates' plan was to wait until most of the hunters were asleep. Then, and only then, would the attack begin.

As they waited in the dark silence, Hook put his mind to what had to be done. How he hated Peter Pan! It was Peter's cheek that annoyed him most. He was such a small child. He was hardly big enough to reach up to Hook's knee, but he was so fearless. And he was always spoiling Hook's plans. Hook felt like a lion in a cage, being bothered by a cheeky sparrow he couldn't catch.

At last the hour had come. Hook rose slowly to his feet and raised his claw. There were yells and screams as the pirates charged the hunters' camp.

Down in their underground house, the children listened to the sound of battle. After a short time, the din stopped as suddenly as it had begun. Which side had won?

'If the hunters have won,' said Tootles, 'they will beat their tom-tom drum. It is always their sign of victory.'

A few seconds later the tom-tom sounded out, just as they all had hoped it would. They cheered for the victory and immediately began to climb up the hollow trees, full of good cheer.

But alas, what met them at the top of the trees was not at all what they expected. The pirates had defeated the hunters, stealing their drum and now they lay in wait to ambush the unsuspecting children.

Curly was the first to emerge from his tree. He climbed out straight into the arms of Starkey, who threw him roughly to the ground where Hook towered over him. The rest of the children were snatched from their trees in the same way, thrown to the ground and then tied up with rope.

'Take them to the ship,' growled Hook. 'Don't let any of them escape.'

The captives were dragged away and Hook was left alone. It had been a great victory, but the greatest prize of all was still missing. Peter had not climbed out of the trees with the rest of the children and was nowhere to be seen. Hook searched around for any sign of him. All he could see was a little twist of smoke rising in the gloomy air.

'Strange,' he said, taking a closer look.

Then he spotted a little chimney sticking up by a tree. A few seconds later he found the biggest hollow tree of all and peered down it into the underground house.

'So *that's* where he's hiding,' said Hook.

He stood very still by the tree, listening for sounds from the house below. He heard nothing.

'The boy is asleep,' he muttered to

himself. 'I will trick him just like I tricked all the others.'

Very quietly, he took off his captain's hat and big black cloak. Then he stepped into the hollow tree and slid smoothly down it. Once inside the house he stood very still, looking about him in the dim light. Then his greedy eyes came to rest on his great prize. Peter lay asleep on the bed, knowing nothing of the pirates' victory over the hunters or the capture of the children.

Hook stepped closer to the bed. He raised his iron claw. Then his red eye caught sight of Peter's cough medicine which was on a table beside his bed.

Hook gave a quiet cackle of delight. He took a tiny bottle out of his pocket – a bottle filled with the most deadly poison known to science. Five drops of this poison were added to Peter's medicine. After one last gloating look at his unsuspecting

victim, Hook climbed out of the house and back up the hollow tree. He wound his cloak around his body, placed his hat on his head and stole away in the blackness of the night.

Peter slept on until he was woken by a soft cautious tapping close by.

'Who's there?' he shouted in alarm.

There was no answer, only another soft tapping.

'Who are you?' he shouted again.

No answer. The tapping seemed to be coming from the door. Peter quickly stepped towards it.

'I won't open this door unless you tell me who you are,' he said.

Then at last the visitor spoke in fairy language, 'Let me in, Peter.'

It was Tinker Bell. Peter quickly opened the door. She flew in and darted about the room in panic. Peter knew something was wrong.

'What is it?' he asked.

'Oh, you'll never guess,' cried Tinker Bell.

'Just tell me,' shouted Peter.

At last Tinker Bell settled and told him all about the capture of Wendy and the children.

'I'll rescue them,' cried Peter, pulling at his sword and raising the cough medicine towards his lips all at the same moment.

'No!' shouted Tinker Bell.

'What?' said Peter, moving the medicine closer to his lips.

'Don't drink the medicine!'

'Why not?' said Peter.

'It's poisoned.'

'Of course it isn't.'

'It is,' cried Tinker Bell. 'Hook poisoned it.'

'Don't be silly. Hook could never come down here,' said Peter, once more raising the medicine to his lips. Tinker Bell could see that there was no time for words and, with one of her lightning movements, got between his lips and the medicine and drank every last drop of it herself. Within a few seconds her wings could hardly carry her.

'It was poisoned, Peter,' she said weakly. 'I'm going to die.'

As her light grew fainter, Tinker Bell's voice tailed off. Peter could hardly hear her.

'What is it, Tinker Bell? What is it?' asked Peter.

And at last he grasped what she was saying. If children believed in fairies she might get well again. It was night-time, so Peter cried out to all the children in the world who might be dreaming of Neverland, 'Do you believe in fairies?'

Immediately Tinker Bell's light shone a little brighter.

'If you believe, clap your hands – then Tinker Bell will live,' shouted Peter.

Peter listened hard. And he heard a wonderful thing! Children all over the world were clapping and believing. So it happened that Tinker Bell sat up and her life was saved. She was soon flying through the room, brighter and naughtier than ever.

'Now to rescue Wendy and the rest of the children,' said Peter.

He left the house just as the moon was

rising and made straight for the pirate ship. It was silent all around and there was no sign of any living thing – except the crocodile, who passed him in the dark shadows.

'Hook or me this time,' said Peter, as he marched onwards towards the final battle.

10

On board the pirate ship

On board the *Jolly Roger*, Hook prowled round the deck. The ship was wrapped in the blanket of night. Starkey and Juke were playing dice and card games, and the other pirates were sprawled across the deck, trying to sleep. Then Hook shouted his order. 'Bring me the lost boys!'

The pirates sprang into action, dragging the child prisoners from the hold of the ship and parading them before Hook. Wendy was tied to the mast.

'They shall walk the plank tonight,' he said. 'But I will save the strongest if they swear to join my pirate gang and say, "Down with Peter Pan!" '

Hook smiled with his teeth clenched. But he didn't smile for long. He'd heard something that filled him with fear. It was the terrible *tick tock* of the crocodile. They all heard it – pirates, boys, Wendy; and everyone turned their heads in one direction. Not towards the crocodile, but towards Hook. Everyone knew that what was about to happen concerned Hook alone and that everyone else could do no more than watch. The ticking came closer and closer. Everyone on the *Jolly Roger* had the same single thought.

The crocodile is about to climb aboard the ship!

The change that came over Hook was

sudden and dramatic. He fell into a little heap crying, 'Hide me.'

The pirates gathered round him. All thoughts of fighting disappeared as fear of what was about to happen gripped them. Only when Hook was completely hidden in the middle of the pirates, did the lost boys dare to sneak a look in the water. And what a surprise they got! For it wasn't a crocodile in the water but Peter, coming to their rescue, and making the *tick tock* sounds himself!

Curly was just about to call out, 'Look, it's Peter!' but Tootles put his hand over his mouth just in time to keep the secret safe. None of the pirates were brave enough to look over the side of the ship, so Peter was able to slide on board without being seen. He quickly untied the boys' ropes. At that moment, the pirates' cook came up on deck. Peter unsheathed his sword and forced him overboard. Then he slipped silently below deck into the cabin.

A second later, Smee said, 'It's gone, Captain. All's still again.'

Hook slowly lifted his head out of hiding and listened hard for the sound of the clock. Nothing. The crocodile had gone. He pulled his body out from under his men.

'Time for a boy to walk the plank,' he cried. 'Fetch the cat o' nine tails, Juke.'

The cat o'nine tails was a whip used to punish sailors, and the very sight of it was enough to put fear into your heart. Juke went below into the cabin to fetch it, but did not return. There was a dull thud from inside the cabin.

'That's where Peter's hiding,' whispered John excitedly.

Slightly was busy counting Peter's victims.

'Two!' he whispered.

'Where's that dog Juke with my cat o'

nine tails?' bellowed Hook. 'Starkey, go and find him.'

Starkey swung himself into the cabin and came back immediately, shouting, 'Juke's been knocked out!'

The boys looked at each other in excitement.

'Get back in that cabin, Starkey, and see what's going on,' shouted Hook.

Starkey cursed and swore but went back into the cabin. There was another dull thud.

'Three!' whispered Slightly.

'What's going on?' shouted Smee in panic.

Hook turned on him, eyes gleaming.

'There's only one way to find out,' said Hook. 'Get in that cabin, Smee.'

'No, by thunder!' screamed Smee. 'Not me.'

'My hook tells me you will,' said Hook, advancing on him with raised claw.

'I'm not going down there,' said Smee.

'You obey captain's orders on this ship, you lubber!' said Hook.

'No! I refuse!'

'Then this is a mutiny and Smee the ringleader,' said Hook.

Smee looked desperately round at the rest of the pirate crew to see if any of them would support him. Nobody dared come to his side.

'You'd better shake hands with the claw,' said Hook, two red dots dancing in his eyes. Smee knew his time was up. He leapt away from Hook on to the big cannon of Long Tom and then threw himself overboard.

'Four!' said Slightly.

'Anyone else in the mood for mutiny?' said Hook, dangerously.

Nobody moved. Nobody spoke. Then Hook grabbed a lantern and said, *'I'll* go into the cabin, you lily-livered lubbers.'

Slightly was getting ready to whisper 'Five!' when Hook came staggering out of the cabin without his lantern.

'Something blew out the light!' he said. 'But Juke and Starkey are down there, knocked out cold.'

'This ship's doomed!' said a pirate in a trembly voice.

Then Hook suddenly had an idea.

'We'll open the cabin door,' said Hook, 'and drive the children in. We've nothing to lose. If they capture whoever's in there, so much the better. If it captures *them*, we're none the worse.'

All that were left of the pirate gang nodded their heads and Wendy, still tied to the ship's mast, let out a scream. The boys, pretending to struggle, were pushed into the cabin. There was dead silence. Then screams and shouts came up from the boys. The pirates put their hands to their ears. Wendy screamed even louder.

'There's never any luck on a pirate ship with a girl on board,' said Hook. 'Throw her overboard!'

All the pirates rushed at Wendy.

'There's nothing that can save you now,' shouted Hook.

But he was wrong. The doors of the cabin burst open and Peter stepped out, sword raised, followed by his army of boys!

'Peter Pan will save you, Wendy!' he said.

Then, turning to the captain, he said, 'It's you or me Hook.'

Hook stepped forward. 'You or me,' he repeated.

Everyone drew back and formed a ring round the two fighters.

'So Pan, this was all your doing,' said Hook.

'It was,' said Peter.

'Then prepare to meet your doom!' screamed Hook.

There were no more words and for a time neither fighter had the upper hand. Peter was a superb swordsman and very fast. But Hook had great strength. He lunged with claw and sword. Peter was forced back by Hook's huge reach but suddenly caught him with his sword. In utter surprise, Hook's sword fell out of his hand. He was at Peter's mercy.

'Now!' shouted all the boys.

But Peter held back to let Hook pick up his sword, and the fight continued. Once again Peter's sword touched Hook and this time Hook abandoned the fight and rushed over to the gunpowder store by Long Tom. He grabbed a lighted torch and held it close to the gunpowder.

'If anyone comes any closer this ship will be blown up!' he said.

But Peter was not afraid and, with his sword raised, he advanced on Hook.

Hook was shaking. He tried to climb

up on to the gun, but tripped and fell overboard – straight into the waiting crocodile's mouth.

11

The return home

When all the rest of the pirates had been captured, the children knew the adventure on Neverland was over.

'Time for home,' said Wendy.

'Can we come too?' asked the lost boys.

'Of course you can,' said Wendy.

Once again, as he had done in the nursery long ago, Peter Pan blew a handful of fairy dust on to the children.

Immediately their bodies began to rise in the air and they began the long journey home.

Mr and Mrs Darling had lived in misery since the disappearance of their children. Mrs Darling had grown sad round the eyes. Mr Darling felt in his bones that he was the one to blame for them going away. He remembered how he'd chained up Nana. Now he often sat in Nana's kennel out in the yard, hoping to teach himself a lesson. Nana missed the children too and would often whimper as she went to each of their empty beds in turn.

One night Mrs Darling said to Nana, 'I had the strangest dream that the children returned.'

The dog put her paw gently into Mrs Darling's lap. Then Mrs Darling began to drop quietly back to sleep. While she was

asleep, the children flew in through the window, and climbed back into their old beds.

When Mrs Darling woke up and went into the nursery, she saw them straight away. But she had seen them like this so often in her dreams that she couldn't believe they were really there. The children waited for a cry of joy, but heard none.

'Mother!' cried Wendy.

'Wendy?' said Mrs Darling, still unsure whether she was dreaming or not.

'Mother!' cried John.

'Mother!' cried Michael.

'My children!' she said, taking hold of all three of them at last, and holding on to them as if she would never let go. Then Mr Darling came running in and the whole family were once again united.

It took some time for things to get back to

normal. Mr and Mrs Darling met the lost boys and took them in as their own children, so they were lost no longer.

After a while, all the boys went to school and the power of flying gradually left them.

Peter Pan had not come with them. He would not grow up like an ordinary boy. He went back to Neverland with Tinker Bell where they both had many more adventures.

But every spring, Peter came back to visit Wendy. As the years passed by she grew up and had her own child, Jane. When Jane grew up she too had a child, called Margaret.

And now, every spring, Peter comes back for Margaret, and takes her off to Neverland, where she plays with Tinker Bell and listens to the mermaids and tells stories to Peter Pan. When Margaret grows up she will have children too, and so it will go on, as long as children never stop believing in fairies . . .

Treasure Island

By Robert Louis Stevenson
Adapted by Peter Ling

Jim's life changes for ever when he finds a treasure map left behind by the pirate Captain Flint, a guest at his mother's inn. He sets sail as a cabin boy on a dangerous voyage to the treasure island, with the mysterious Long John Silver and his crew. But they seem to know far more about the island than they're willing to tell . . .